Comma Quest

The Rules They Followed
The Sentences They Saved

Lesley Roessing

Illustrated by Miles Bodimeade

Discover Writing

To Dad, Marsha, Meg, and Matt, who literally brought music into my life, and to Max and Dean, our future music. Thanks to Bobbi Westermeier and Alexis Zambino
who orginiated the song for the introductory-prepositional phrase rule.
~L.R.

To Georgy and Holly, as always.
Oh, and to Paul Period 'cos I hope he's doing okay.
~M.B.

ISBN: 978-1-931492-30-0
Library of Congress control number available on request

Published by Discover Writing, Inc.
www.discoverwriting.com

Printed in The United States of America
Illustrations by Miles Bodimeade
Book and cover design by Bookwrights

17 16 15 14 13   10 9 8 7 6 5 4 3 2 1

Momma Comma looked around in dismay. She had lived in this sentence all her life. She had raised her children here and had watched the sentence expand over time. This was her home, but her sentence no longer made sense.

She read it over.

Sue, and John, went, to, the corner, grocery, store, Mom.

There were too many commas, too many pauses.

I've got to get these kids out of the sentence. It's time for them to find sentences of their own.

3

She faced her children: Carl, Connie, Christie, Corey, and the twins Cassie and Cathy.

They had been hanging around the sentence much too long. Momma had not noticed that her family had been growing. And the children were becoming older. It was time for them to go. She hoped that she had trained them to find sentences of their own.

Momma held a family meeting.

"Children, you are all grown up. As much as I love having you in the sentence, we are no longer helping it to make sense. We have to remember that our purpose is to provide only significant pauses."

She paused for effect, but it came out more as a sigh.

Momma showed them their home sentence as it had originally been written.

Sue and John went to the corner grocery store, Mom.

"Someone is telling Mother that Sue and John went to the corner grocery store. They are directly addressing Mom. Remember the Direct Address Rule song we sing to the tune of "Head and Shoulders, Knees, and Toes"?

Comma before direct address: "Hi, Momma!"
Comma after direct address: "Momma, Hi!"
Commas all around di-rect address.
"'Hi, Momma Comma, Hi."

Everyone nodded as they sang along.

"However, as our family grew, this sentence began to make less sense. It has become a senseless sentence—a <u>nonsense</u>ntence."
Momma laughed at her own joke.

"But where shall we go?" asked Christie.

"You will go where you are needed," Momma calmly replied. "You have grown up learning the comma rules. It is now time to follow those rules and find sentences that need to be saved.

"You can look in libraries, schools, bookstores, and even office buildings. Anywhere writers are writing, they are sure to need commas. You can help them get their sentences right, bringing more meaning to their words."

Carl was the independent one. He went first, taking off by himself. He crawled into the local school. He had heard that these new writers needed help.

Inching his way down the hall, he saw the sign on a door:

Writing Workshop Today

Eureka! I have hit the jackpot! And Mom did say, "Go where you are needed."

Carl edged down the aisles, climbed on seatbacks, and looked over shoulders.

Then he saw it:

After he ate his snack John went straight home.

His mother's favorite song played in his head to the tune of "If You're Happy and You Know It":

Put a comma after an introductory clause.
Put a comma after an introductory clause.
Put a comma after the clause
so you know just when to pause.
Put a comma after an introductory clause.

There was the introductory clause:

"**After** [subordinating conjunction] **he** [subject] **ate** [verb]"

Carl smiled and jumped.

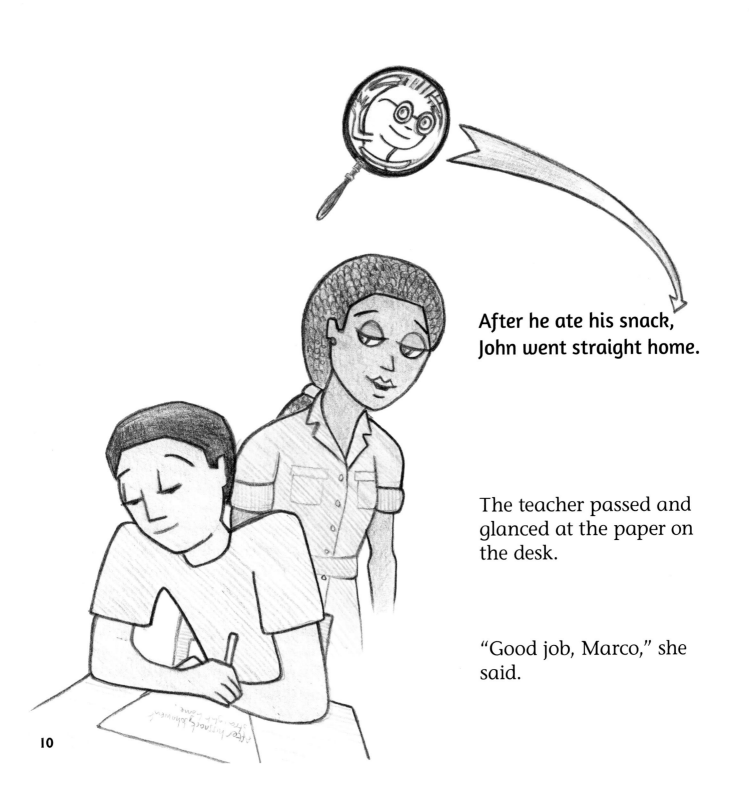

After he ate his snack, John went straight home.

The teacher passed and glanced at the paper on the desk.

"Good job, Marco," she said.

Connie set off next. She actually was relieved. Her fiancé Cody had been struggling with a sentence that contained a nonessential (unnecessary) clause. The writer had made the common mistake of setting off the clause with only one comma. Cody had been asking Connie to marry him and move into the sentence before the writer inserted another comma on his own.

Connie kissed her mother and siblings goodbye and took off.

She passed a sentence:

Shakira who liked the taste of lemons bought lemonade.

Nope, that clause is essential (necessary) to the meaning of the sentence. Shakira bought lemonade **because** *she liked the taste of lemons. The clause, "who liked the taste of lemons," cannot be taken out.*

There he was!

**Sue, who took longer to decide
bought some lemonade and pretzels.**

Connie could see that Cody needed her to help with that clause. It was one that could be removed. It was unnecessary to the meaning of the sentence, a nonessential clause. Sue's taking longer to decide what to buy was not necessary (essential) to the fact that she bought the lemonade and pretzels.

Momma's song rang in her ear, again to the tune of "If You're Happy and You Know It":

Put commas 'round a nonessential clause.
Put commas 'round a nonessential clause.
Put commas all about –
    So you can take it out.
Put commas 'round a nonessential clause.

Cody," she called out, "I will marry you and live in your sentence."
Two minutes later they were wed and living together in their own
sentence.

Sue, who took longer to decide, bought some lemonade and pretzels.

Meanwhile, the twins, Cathy and Cassie, were worried. They had never been separated. Since birth they had lived next to each other in their home sentence. Where would they find a sentence that required TWO commas—close together?

Quickly they ran through the Comma Rules.

"Got it!" exclaimed Cassie. "We have to find a sentence with items in a series—but not too many."

"What kind of items?" asked Cathy. She remembered the rules but didn't understand all of them.

"Three words—nouns, verbs, adjectives—any part of speech will do. Also phrases and clauses. But they have to be connected with only one conjunction, a coordinating conjunction."

"What's a *conjunction*?" Cathy hadn't listened too well in the past.

Momma had songs for EVERYTHING.
Cassie sang to the tune of "The Farmer in the Dell."

Conjunctions are joiners,
Conjunctions are joiners,
AND-OR-BUT-NOR-YET-FOR
Conjunctions are joiners
and SO,

CONJUNCTION

"Oh, I remember. That's just the Chorus; there's more…"

Conjunctions join words,
Conjunctions join words,
AND-OR-BUT-NOR-YET-FOR
Conjunctions join words
and SO,

Conjunctions join phrases,
Conjunctions join phrases,
AND-OR-BUT-NOR-YET-FOR
Conjunctions join phrases
and SO,

Conjunctions join clauses,
Conjunctions join clauses,
AND-OR-BUT-NOR-YET-FOR
Conjunctions join clauses
and SO, [repeat Chorus]

Cassie sang along, glad that Cathy now understood conjunctions and their function as "joiners."

Momma had also taught them a song to remember the rule for using commas with items (words, phrases, or clauses) in a series.

Cassie sang Momma Comma's song to the tune of "Row, Row, Row Your Boat."

ONE comma, TWO comma, conjunction THREE
Items in a series;
ONE comma, TWO comma, conjunction THREE
Items in a series.

WORD comma, WORD comma, conjunction WORD
SINGLE WORDS in a series;
WORD comma, WORD comma, conjunction WORD
SINGLE WORDS in a series.

And last,

PHRASE comma, PHRASE comma, conjunction PHRASE
PHRASES in a series;
CLAUSE comma, CLAUSE comma, conjunction CLAUSE
Also CLAUSES in a series.

Cathy was impressed. She didn't realize that these rules could be so easy to understand—and sing!

The twins separated, looking for the perfect sentence in which they could *both* live together.

It didn't take long. "Items in a series" is one of the most common rules of commas. Cathy saw the sentence first.

John bought chips juice and a comic book.

"Look, Cassie, a sentence and a series of three nouns! And it's in a classroom storybook."

Cassie was proud of her sister. Cathy had learned this rule so quickly. If they joined this sentence, they would be able to stay together. They held hands and jumped.

"Let's go…."

John bought chips, juice, and a comic book.

Christie had her own problems. She was jealous of Connie now that Connie had found true love and was married. Instead of looking for a sentence, Christie was looking for a boyfriend. She knew she had to be careful.

Last time she had fallen, and fallen hard, for Paul. She hadn't realized that Paul was a period. She thought he had just lost his comma "tail."

Christie wasn't prejudiced against other punctuation, but Paul Period had wanted to turn her into a semicolon (;). She wanted to join him in a sentence but only as the comma she was.

Momma had warned her children about punctuation marks who might want them to change. Some just didn't see the value in commas.

"Pause?" Paul had said. "You only want to make them *pause*? As a semicolon, we can make them *STOP*— at least for a little while!"

Christie had broken up with Paul and was still looking for true love.

Then she saw it. Two simple sentences that just had to be joined together:

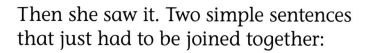
Sue stopped at Joan's house.
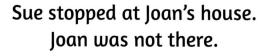
Joan was not there.

Each of these sentences was short, choppy, with no rhythm. But *together* they could sing.

21

As the family romantic, this was Christie's favorite rule—using a comma and a conjunction to join independent clauses (or simple sentences) into a compound sentence.

Momma wrote a romantic rule song just for her, to the tune of "Bingo."

An independent clause met an independent clause,
And they fell in love together.
Comma, Conjunction — Comma, Conjunction
Comma, Conjunction,
And they fell in love together.
An independent clause married an independent clause,
And they were joined together.
Comma, Conjunction — Comma, Conjunction
Comma, Conjunction,
A compound sentence for-ever.

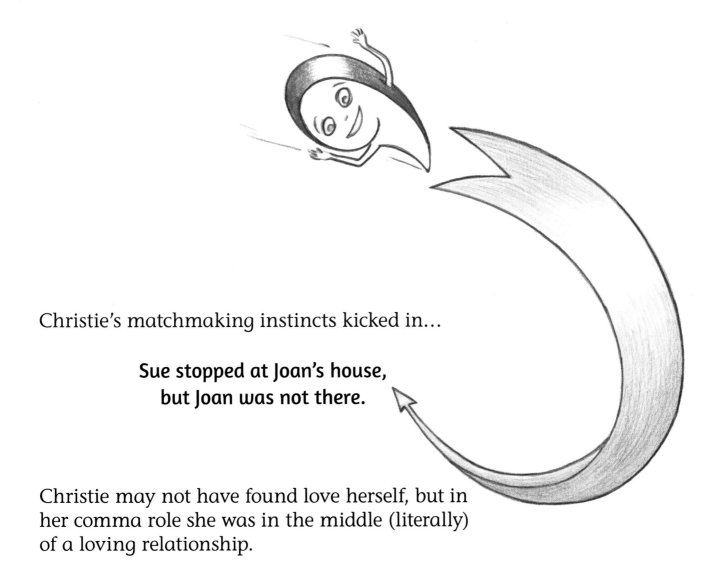

Christie's matchmaking instincts kicked in...

**Sue stopped at Joan's house,
but Joan was not there.**

Christie may not have found love herself, but in her comma role she was in the middle (literally) of a loving relationship.

Corey was the last to leave. He loved living in his home sentence and did not want to go out on his own. Additionally, everyone else had followed the easiest rules. There was one rule left:

Put a comma after two or more introductory phrases.

Corey racked his brain. *What's a phrase?*

He asked Momma. She began singing to the tune of "Love and Marriage":

Preposition and noun
Preposition and noun
Go together like a circus and clown.
This I tell you, brother,
You can't have one without the other.

Momma continued singing.
She couldn't resist singing a good song.

Preposition and noun
Preposition and noun
Go together like a king and crown.
This I tell you, brother,
You can't have one without the other.

Suddenly Corey remembered. This was the song where they all had their own verses. His special line was "Go together like up and down." That's what a phrase is—a preposition and a noun: *down the street; in the air; around the block; near the store.*

Corey spied a sentence with one, no, two, phrases—*after a walk* and *in the park.* They were both at the beginning of a sentence.

After a walk in the park Sue went home and found that Cindy had told her mother about the shopping trip.

Corey next tried to remember exactly how the "double phrase" comma rule worked. He remembered his brother and sisters singing a song to "The Brady Bunch Theme":

Here's a story of a little comma
Who was bringing up two phrases on its own.
Then those phrases joined a simple sentence,
And now they're not alone.
Two introduct'ry phrases
Two introduct'ry phrases
Put a comma after two introduct'ry phrases.

That's it. I get it!

"Bye, Momma. I see where I am needed…."

Corey, the last to leave the home sentence, moved into his new home.

After a walk in the park, Sue went home and found that Cindy had told her mother about the shopping trip.

Momma looked around. Her sentence certainly felt empty even though it now made sense again.

What have I done, convincing my little commas to find sentences of their own?

In panic she looked around the whole page.

AND there they all were, not far away: Carl, Connie (and husband Cody), Christie, Corey, and the twins Cassie and Cathy. True, they were living in their own sentences, but together all their sentences had become part of the same story:

"Cindy, where are your sister and brother?"

"Sue and John went to the corner grocery store, Mom."

There were no snacks at home; their mother had not gone shopping in days. Sue and John, the 12 year old twins, decided to go shopping on their own without their mother's permission.

John bought chips, juice, and a comic book.

Sue, who took longer to decide , bought some lemonade and pretzels.

After John ate his snacks, he went straight home.

Sue stopped at Joan's house, but Joan was not there.

After a walk in the park, Sue went home and found that Cindy had told her mother about the shopping trip.

Sue and John were grounded for a week!

THE 6 COMMA RULES

1. Place a comma to set off nouns of direct address.

2. Put a comma after an introductory adverbial clause.

3. Put commas around a nonessential clause [or participial phrase].

4. Separate items of a series with commas.

5. Use commas to separate independent clauses when they are joined by a coordinating conjunction.

6. Place a comma after two introductory phrases.

Follow this link to listen to all of Comma Momma's songs and record some of your own!

http://snd.sc/1fKplly

Rule 1 Direct Address
(to the tune "Head and Shoulders, Knees and Toes." Clap for the commas)

Comma before direct address: "Hi, Momma!"
Comma after direct address: "Momma, Hi!"
Commas all around di-rect address."'
Hi, Momma Comma, "Hi."

Rule 2 Introductory Clause
(to the tune "If You're Happy and You Know it")

Put a comma after an introductory clause.
Put a comma after an introductory clause.
Put a comma after the clause
so you know just when to pause.
Put a comma after an introductory clause.

Rule 3 Nonessential Clause
(to the tune "If You're Happy and You Know it.")

Put commas 'round a nonessential clause.
Put commas 'round a nonessential clause.
Put commas all about – so you can take it out.
Put commas 'round a nonessential clause.

Song Conjunctions are Joiners
(to the tune "The Farmer and the Dell")

Conjunctions are joiners,
Conjunctions are joiners,
AND-OR-BUT-NOR-YET-FOR
Conjunctions are joiners,
and SO,

Conjunctions join words,
Conjunctions join words,
AND-OR-BUT-NOR-YET-FOR
Conjunctions join words,
and SO,

Conjunctions join phrases,
Conjunctions join phrases,
AND-OR-BUT-NOR-YET-FOR
Conjunctions join phrases,
and SO,

Conjunctions join clauses,
Conjunctions join clauses,
AND-OR-BUT-NOR-YET-FOR
Conjunctions join clauses,
and SO,
[repeat Chorus]

Rule 4: Items in a series
(to the tune "Row, Row, Row your Boat")

ONE comma, TWO comma,
conjunction THREE
Items in a series;
ONE comma, TWO comma,
conjunction THREE
Items in a series.
WORD comma, WORD comma,
conjunction WORD
SINGLE WORDS in a series;
WORD comma, WORD comma,
conjunction WORD
SINGLE WORDS in a series.
PHRASE comma, PHRASE comma,
conjunction PHRASE
PHRASES in a series;
CLAUSE comma, CLAUSE comma,
conjunction CLAUSE
Also CLAUSES in a series

Rule 5: Compound Sentences
(to the tune "Bingo")

An independent clause met an independent clause,
And they fell in love together.
Comma, Conjunction — Comma, Conjunction
Comma, Conjunction,
And they fell in love together.
An independent clause married an independent clause,
And they were joined together.
Comma, Conjunction — Comma, Conjunction
Comma, Conjunction,
A compound sentence for-ever.

Rule 6: Double Introductory phrases
(sung to "The Brady Bunch Theme")

Here's a story of a little comma
Who was bringing up two phrases on its own.
Then those phrases joined a simple sentence,
And now they're not alone.
Two introduct'ry phrases
Two introduct'ry phrases
Put a comma after two introduct'ry phrases.

Song Preposition and Noun
(to "Love and Marriage")

Preposition and noun
Preposition and noun
Go together like a circus and clown
This I tell you, brother,
You can't have one without the other.

Preposition and noun
Preposition and noun
Go together like a king and crown.
This I tell you, brother,
You can't have one without the other.

Preposition and noun
Preposition and noun
Go together like up and down.
This I tell you, brother,
You can't have one without the other.

THE END